CHRISTMAS BELLS ARE RINGING

BOOKS BY
JOHN E. BREWTON

UNDER THE TENT OF THE SKY

GAILY WE PARADE

With SARA BREWTON

BRIDLED WITH RAINBOWS

CHRISTMAS BELLS ARE RINGING

INDEX TO CHILDREN'S POETRY

CHRISTMAS BELLS
ARE RINGING

A Treasury of Christmas Poetry

SELECTED BY

SARA and JOHN E. BREWTON

Illustrations by DECIE MERWIN

THE MACMILLAN COMPANY · NEW YORK

ACKNOWLEDGMENTS

For permission to reprint the poems included in CHRISTMAS BELLS ARE RINGING ap-
preciation is expressed to the following publishers and authors:—

Appleton-Century-Crofts, Inc., New York, for "Christmas Singing," by Elsie Williams
Chandler from St. Nicholas Magazine (Copyright, 1929, by The Century Company, reprinted
by permission of Appleton-Century-Crofts, Inc.); and for "Not Only in the Christmas-Tide,"
from When Life Is Young by Mary Mapes Dodge (Copyright, 1894, 1922, The Century Company, reprinted by permission of Appleton-Century-Crofts, Inc.).

Blackwell & Mott, Ltd., Oxford, England, for "The Holly," by Edith King.

Child Life, Inc., Boston, for "The Christmas Exchange," by Arthur Guiterman (Copyright,
1941, by Child Life, Inc.); "Kris Kringle," by Clinton Scollard (Copyright, 1923, by Child
Life, Inc.); and "The Shepherd Left Behind," by Mildred Plew Merryman (Copyright, 1933,
by Child Life, Inc.).

The Commonweal, New York, for "Juniper," by Eileen Duggan.

Coward-McCann, Inc., New York, for "The Barn," from Compass Rose by Elizabeth Coats-
worth (Copyright, 1929, by Coward-McCann, Inc., reprinted by permission of Coward-McCann,
Inc.); for "In the Stable," from Songs and Verses by Elizabeth Goudge (Copyright, 1948, by
Elizabeth Goudge, reprinted by permission of Coward-McCann, Inc.).

J. M. Dent & Sons, Ltd., London, for distribution throughout the world excluding the United
States, for "A Christmas Carol," from The Wild Knight and Other Stories by G. K. Chesterton.

Doubleday & Company, Inc., New York, for "Christmas-Time," from Fairies and Friends by
Rose Fyleman (Copyright, 1926, by Doubleday & Company); "Winnipeg at Christmas," from
Gay Go Up by Rose Fyleman (Copyright, 1929, 1930, by Doubleday & Company, Inc.).

Gerald Duckworth & Co., Ltd. for distribution rights in the British Empire market for "In
the Stable," from Songs and Verses by Elizabeth Goudge.

E. P. Dutton & Company, New York, for "A Christmas Carol," from The Wild Knight and
Other Stories by G. K. Chesterton (Copyright, 1914, by E. P. Dutton & Company).

Follett Publishing Company for "Come, Ride with Me to Toyland," from Songs from Around
a Toadstool Table by Rowena Bennett (Copyright, 1930, 1937, by Follett Publishing Company).

Harper & Brothers, New York, for "Christmas in the Woods," by Frances Frost (Copyright,
1942, by Frances Frost); "School After Christmas," from Bread an' Jam by Wymond Garth-
waite (Copyright, 1928, by Harper & Brothers); and "Counting the Days," "Do Not Open
Until Christmas," and "I Like Christmas," from Counting the Days by James S. Tippett
(Copyright, 1940, by Harper & Brothers).

Houghton Mifflin Company, Boston, for "The Joy of Giving," by John Greenleaf Whittier,
and "A Real Santa Claus," from Little Folk Lyrics by Frank Dempster Sherman (Copyright,
1897, by Houghton Mifflin Company).

J. B. Lippincott Company, Philadelphia, for "Annar-Mariar's Christmas Shopping," "For
Them," "In the Week When Christmas Comes," and "Through a Shop Window," from Come

iv

TO

the Happy Little Boy
Whose First Christmas
Was Spent at
Merrylog Farm

Then let your hearts be filled with joy,
While Christmas bells are ringing,
And keep the birthday of the Lord
With merriment and singing.

—Mary Jane Carr

FOREWORD

Christmas is a happy time, for
   . . . not a child but keeps some trace
   Of Christmas secrets in his face.
What joy to go shopping
      Now that it's Christmas time
      To see the little shops all decked
      Gay as a pantomime,
and to walk on the city streets
      Seeing the sights of Christmas,
         Smelling each Christmas smell.
What delight is ours in the home as we
      Bring forth the holly,
         The box, and the bay,
and
      Deck out our cottage
         For glad Christmas-day.
How jolly when Santa Claus comes with his shout of:
      Happy Christmas to all, and to all a good night.
But happiest are we when sharing our Christmas cheer. So
      Before you gather round the tree
      To dance the day about,
      Oh please to give a little glee
      To them that go without.
Christmas is a holy time, a hallowed time.
      Christmas is remembering
      Shy shepherds on a hill
      And voices echoing
      "Peace—Good Will!"
So hallowed is the time that on
      Christmas morn, the legends say,
      Even the cattle kneel to pray,
      Even the beasts of wood and field
      Homage to Christ the Saviour yield.

ix

In *Christmas Bells Are Ringing* are the poems about the happy and the hallowed Christmas time which we have found delightful. In the spirit of Christmas, we wish to share them with you.

August 15, 1951

Sara Westbrook Brewton
John E. Brewton

CONTENTS

IN THE WEEK WHEN CHRISTMAS COMES

HOW FULL THE GLITTERING SHOPS ARE NOW

LET EVERY HALL HAVE BOUGHS OF GREEN

THE LATCH-STRING'S HANGING AT THE DOOR

SANTA CLAUS COMES

FRIENDLY BEASTS AROUND HIM STOOD

WHO WILL KNEEL THEM GENTLY DOWN

NOT ONLY IN THE CHRISTMAS-TIDE

xiv

IN THE WEEK
WHEN CHRISTMAS COMES

Let every pudding burst with plums,
And every tree bear dolls and drums,
In the week when Christmas comes.

—*Eleanor Farjeon*

IN THE WEEK WHEN CHRISTMAS COMES

This is the week when Christmas comes.

Let every pudding burst with plums,
And every tree bear dolls and drums,
   In the week when Christmas comes.

Let every hall have boughs of green,
With berries glowing in between,
   In the week when Christmas comes.

Let every doorstep have a song
Sounding the dark street along,
   In the week when Christmas comes.

Let every steeple ring a bell
With a joyful tale to tell,
   In the week when Christmas comes.

Let every night put forth a star
To show us where the heavens are,
   In the week when Christmas comes.

Let every stable have a lamb
Sleeping warm beside its dam,
   In the week when Christmas comes.

This is the week when Christmas comes.
          —Eleanor Farjeon

CHRISTMAS-TIME

The church bells at Christmas-time
  Ring all about the town;
The gay folk at Christmas-time
  Go walking up and down;
They smile at me, they smile at you,
  The streets and squares are smiling too.

In every house at Christmas-time
  Are pretty sights to see;
    And strange things at Christmas-time
  Do grow upon a tree;
And one for me and one for you,
  And isn't it a sweet to-do?

          —*Rose Fyleman*

I LIKE CHRISTMAS

I'm sure that I like Christmas best
Of any time
In all the year.

I like to help bring loads of greens
And put them up
For Christmas cheer.

I like to open packages
And help prepare
Good things to eat,

Or go a-caroling at night
With all my friends
Along the street.

I like to think of Santa Claus
And help to decorate
Our Tree.

Yes, I am sure that Christmas is
The best time
Of the year for me.

—James S. Tippett

SIMPLE SAM

Said Simple Sam: "Does Christmas come
  In April or December,
In winter, spring, or harvest time?
  I really can't remember."
               —*Leroy F. Jackson*

COUNTING THE DAYS

How many days to Christmas?
Forty, thirty, and then—
Twenty-five, twenty, seventeen,
Fourteen, eleven, ten.

Nine eight seven—six five four—
Three days, two days slowly go.
But the last day before Christmas
Is—slow—slow—slow.
               —*James S. Tippett*

WINNIPEG AT CHRISTMAS

In Winnipeg at Christmas
  There's lots and lots of snow,
Very clean and crisp and hard
And glittering like a Christmas card
  Everywhere you go;
Snow upon the housetops,
  Snow along the street,
And QUEEN VICTORIA in her chair
Has snow upon her stony hair
  And snow upon her feet.

6

In Winnipeg at Christmas
 They line the street with trees—
Christmas trees lit up at night
With little balls of coloured light
 As pretty as you please.
The people hurry past you
 In furry boots and wraps;
The sleighs are like a picture book
And all the big policemen look
 Like Teddy bears in caps.

And, oh! the smiling ladies
 And jolly girls and boys;
And, oh! the parties and the fun,
With lovely things for everyone—
 Books and sweets and toys.
So, if some day at Christmas
 You don't know where to go,
Just pack your boxes up, I beg,
And start at once for Winnipeg;
 You'd like it there, I know.
     —Rose Fyleman

CHRISTMAS IN THE HEART

It is Christmas in the mansion,
   Yule-log fires and silken frocks;
It is Christmas in the cottage,
   Mother's filling little socks.

It is Christmas on the highway,
   In the thronging, busy mart;
But the dearest, truest Christmas
   Is the Christmas in the heart.
              —Author Unknown

CHRISTMAS IS REMEMBERING

Christmas is remembering
Shy shepherds on a hill
And voices echoing
"Peace—Good Will!"

Christmas is remembering
A stable and a star
And wise men journeying
From afar.

Christmas is remembering
A new-born baby boy
And all the world caroling
Songs of joy.
          —Elsie Binns

PATAPAN

A BURGUNDIAN CHRISTMAS CAROL

Willie, take your little drum,
With your whistle, Robin, come!
  When we hear the fife and drum
Ture-lure-lu, pata-pata-pan,
    When we hear the fife and drum
    Christmas should be frolicsome.

Thus the men of olden days
Loved the King of Kings to praise:
  When they hear the fife and drum,
Ture-lure-lu, pata-pata-pan,
    When they hear the fife and drum,
    Sure our children won't be dumb!

God and man are now become
More at one than fife and drum.
  When you hear the fife and drum,
Ture-lure-lu, pata-pata-pan,
    When you hear the fife and drum
    Dance, and make the village hum!
            —*Bernard De La Monnoye*

AN ALPHABET OF CHRISTMAS

A for the animals out in the stable.

B for the Babe in their manger for cradle.

C for the Carols so blithe and gay.

D for December, the twenty-fifth day.

E for the Eve when we're all so excited.

F for the Fire when the Yule Log is lighted.

G is the Goose which you all know is fat.

H is the Holly you stick in your hat.

I for the Ivy which clings to the wall.

J is for Jesus the cause of it all.

K for the Kindness begot by this feast.

L is the Light shining way in the East.

M for the Mistletoe. Beware where it hangs!

N is the Nowell the angels first sang.

O for the Oxen, the first to adore Him.

P for the Presents Wise Men laid before Him.

Q for the Queerness that this should have been,
Near two thousand years before you were seen.

R for the Romps and the Raisins and Nuts.

S for the Stockings that Santa Claus stuffs.

T for the Toys on the Christmas Tree hanging.

U is for Us over all the world ranging.

V for the Visitors welcomed so warmly.

W the Waits at your doors singing heartily!

X Y Z bother me! All I can say,

Is this is the end of my Christmas lay.

So now to you all, wherever you be,

A merry merry Christmas, and many may you see!

—Author Unknown

THE FIRST DAY OF CHRISTMAS

The first day of Christmas,
My true love sent to me
A partridge in a pear tree.

The second day of Christmas,
My true love sent to me
Two turtle doves, and
A partridge in a pear tree.

The third day of Christmas,
My true love sent to me
Three French hens,
Two turtle doves, and
A partridge in a pear tree.

The fourth day of Christmas,
My true love sent to me
Four colly birds,
Three French hens,
Two turtle doves, and
A partridge in a pear tree.

The fifth day of Christmas,
My true love sent to me
Five gold rings,
Four colly birds,
Three French hens,
Two turtle doves, and
A partridge in a pear tree.

The sixth day of Christmas,
My true love sent to me
Six geese a-laying,
Five gold rings,
Four colly birds,

Three French hens,
Two turtle doves, and
A partridge in a pear tree.

The seventh day of Christmas,
My true love sent to me
Seven swans a-swimming,
Six geese a-laying,
Five gold rings,
Four colly birds,
Three French hens,
Two turtle doves, and
A partridge in a pear tree.

The eighth day of Christmas,
My true love sent to me
Eight maids a-milking,
Seven swans a-swimming,
Six geese a-laying,
Five gold rings,
Four colly birds,
Three French hens,
Two turtle doves, and
A partridge in a pear tree.

The ninth day of Christmas,
My true love sent to me
Nine drummers drumming,
Eight maids a-milking,
Seven swans a-swimming,
Six geese a-laying,
Five gold rings,
Four colly birds,
Three French hens,
Two turtle doves, and
A partridge in a pear tree.

The tenth day of Christmas,
My true love sent to me
Ten pipers piping,
Nine drummers drumming,
Eight maids a-milking,
Seven swans a-swimming,
Six geese a-laying,
Five gold rings,
Four colly birds,
Three French hens,
Two turtle doves, and
A partridge in a pear tree.

The eleventh day of Christmas,
My true love sent to me
Eleven ladies dancing,
Ten pipers piping,
Nine drummers drumming,
Eight maids a-milking,
Seven swans a-swimming,
Six geese a-laying,
Five gold rings,
Four colly birds,
Three French hens,
Two turtle doves, and
A partridge in a pear tree.

The twelfth day of Christmas,
My true love sent to me
Twelve fiddlers fiddling,
Eleven ladies dancing,
Ten pipers piping,
Nine drummers drumming,
Eight maids a-milking,
Seven swans a-swimming,

Six geese a-laying,
Five gold rings,
Four colly birds,
Three French hens,
Two turtle doves, and
A partridge in a pear tree.
—*Author Unknown*

BEGGAR'S RHYME

Christmas is coming, the geese are getting fat,
Please to put a penny in the old man's hat;
If you haven't got a penny, a ha'penny will do,
If you haven't got a ha'penny, God bless you.
—*Author Unknown*

FOR CHRISTMAS

Now not a window small or big
But wears a wreath or holly sprig;
Nor any shop too poor to show
Its spray of pine or mistletoe.
Now city airs are spicy-sweet
With Christmas trees along each street,
Green spruce and fir whose boughs will hold
Their tinseled balls and fruits of gold.
Now postmen pass in threes and fours
Like bent, blue-coated Santa Claus.
Now people hurry to and fro
With little girls and boys in tow,
And not a child but keeps some trace
Of Christmas secrets in his face.
—*Rachel Field*

HOW FULL THE
GLITTERING SHOPS ARE NOW

How full the glittering shops are now
   With chattering tongues and open purses,
And children scrambling anyhow
   Beside their mothers, aunts, and nurses.

                    —*Eleanor Farjeon*

THROUGH A SHOP WINDOW

How full the glittering shops are now
  With chattering tongues and open purses,
And children scrambling anyhow
  Beside their mothers, aunts, and nurses;
With eager eyes and laughing lips,
  And problems of a thousand choices,
With loaded trees, and lucky dips,
  And Christmas-time in all the voices!
You scarce can push your way along
  Behind the window—which discloses
Outside the little ragged throng
  With longing eyes and flattened noses.
                    —*Eleanor Farjeon*

CHRISTMAS SHOPPERS

Oh, the wind is brisk and biting
and the cold is not inviting,
but there's music, merry music everywhere.
The streets are full of bustle,
and our feet are full of hustle,
for there's Christmas, merry Christmas in the air.

Oh, the wind is cold and chilly
and it whistles at us shrilly,
but there's music, merry music everywhere.
The bells are full of ringing
and our hearts are full of singing,
for there's Christmas, merry Christmas in the air.
                    —*Aileen Fisher*

ANNAR-MARIAR'S CHRISTMAS SHOPPING

Annar-Mariar-Elizar Smith
Looked in the Baker's window with
Her brother Willyum by the hand.
"Look!" she said, "Willyum! ain't it grand!
See them puddin's done up in basins—
They're all stuffed full of currints and raisins!
We'll 'ave that big 'un there, Willyum, see,
Fer dinner on Chrismuss Day, you an' me.
See them Chrismuss Cakes white and pink,
With holly and bells! Would you like, d'you think,
The one with the snowballs and funny man?
What, that with the robins? All right, you can."

Annar-Mariar-Elizar Smith
Stopped at the Greengrocer's, where the pith
Of its beautiful wonders were seen outside.
"Look at the Chrismuss-trees, duck!" she cried.
"Which'll we 'ave sent 'ome? That tall
'Un there'll do beautiful for us all!
And that little tiny'll be jest right
Fer Baby to see when she wakes at night.
We'll 'ave that bundle of 'olly, oo!
And that mistletoe there!—we'll tell 'em to
Send nuts, and bananers, and tangerines,
And apples, along o' the evergreens."

Annar-Mariar-Elizar Smith
Saw in the Toyshop a world of myth
And fairytale. "Oo!" she chuckled, "see
The dolls, and the crackers, and all! The tree
'Ll look lovely with some of them shiny things,
And the Fairy Queen with the silvery wings,
And the Father Chrismuss, and sparkly chains,

And the teaset fer me, and the box of trains
Fer you, and the farmyard fer Baby, wot?
Sha'n't we serprise 'er with all we've got!"
Then Annar and Willyum home did run
With the whole of their Christmas shopping done.
                    —Eleanor Farjeon

SECRETS ·

If you see a package
Gaily wrapped and tied,
Don't ask too many questions,
'Cause a secret is inside.
                    —E. Kathryn Fowler

DO NOT OPEN UNTIL CHRISTMAS ·

I shake-shake,
Shake-shake,
Shake the package well.

But what there is
Inside of it,
Shaking will not tell.
                    —James S. Tippett

BUNDLES

A bundle is a funny thing,
It always sets me wondering;
For whether it is thin or wide
You never know just what's inside.

Especially on Christmas week,
Temptation is so great to peek!
Now wouldn't it be much more fun
If shoppers carried things undone?
                              —*John Farrar*

EIGHTH STREET WEST

I will go walking on Eighth Street
    Now that it's Christmas time
To see the little shops all decked
    Gay as a pantomime.
There will be patchwork and Russian smocks;
    Angels of marzipan;
Green glass bottles and picture books
    In their jackets spick and span.
There will be knickknacks of painted wood;
    Candles for every tree
Stacked at the curb in spicy green
    Bristling and needle-y.
There will be children and dogs about;
    Organ men to play,
And people carrying parcels home,
    Hurrying on their way.
I will go walking on Eighth Street
    From Avenue to "L,"
Seeing the sights of Christmas,
    Smelling each Christmas smell.
                              —*Rachel Field*

20

LET EVERY HALL
HAVE BOUGHS OF GREEN

Now not a window small or big
But wears a wreath or holly sprig;
Nor any shop too poor to show
Its spray of pine or mistletoe.

—*Rachel Field*

HOLLY FAIRIES

Oh, fairies love a holly tree
The foliage makes a roof
  of sturdy shingles,
  always green
and new and weatherproof.
And even under winter skies
the berries burn so bright
they look like
  little fairy lamps,
with bulbs of crimson light.

Oh, fairies love a holly spray
too much by far to leave,
and so they up and follow it
indoors, on Christmas Eve.
And that is why each house
  is blessed
where holly sprigs are seen,
because the fairies
  still are there
beneath the red and green.
                  —Aileen Fisher

CHRISTMAS GREETING

Sing hey! Sing hey!
For Christmas Day;
Twine mistletoe and holly,
For friendship glows
In winter snows,
And so let's all be jolly.
—*Author Unknown*

BUT GIVE ME HOLLY, BOLD AND JOLLY

But give me holly, bold and jolly,
Honest, prickly, shining holly;
Pluck me holly leaf and berry
For the day when I make merry.
—*Christina G. Rossetti*

24

THE HOLLY

How happy the holly-tree looks, and how strong,
Where he stands like a sentinel all the year long.

Neither dry summer heat nor cold winter hail
Can make that gay warrior tremble or quail.

He has beamed all the year, but bright scarlet he'll glow
When the ground glitters white with the fresh fallen snow.

—*Edith King*

MISTLETOE SPRITES

Wee sprites have followed mistletoe
Since pagan days of long ago.
In tight soft breeches, dusty green,
The little folk can scarce be seen,
But pearly buttons fasten tight
Their tiny jackets, left and right,
And sometimes on the mistletoe
A bunch of buttons softly glow.
We call them berries, but it's clear
When we see berries, sprites are near.
And wherever these folks go
Good luck comes with mistletoe!

—*Solveig Paulson Russell*

ROUND AND ROUND

Twist the tinsel,
    Flashing bright,
Round the tree
    For our delight.
Twining, shining,
    Overhead,
Wind the lights of
    Green and red.
Now join hands, and
    So will we
Circle round the
    Christmas tree,
Singing still the
    Holy word
That the watching
    Shepherds heard:
"Peace on earth,
    Good will to men"—
Jesus' birthday
    Comes again!
                —*Dorothy Brown Thompson*

CHRISTMAS TREE

I'll find me a spruce
in the cold white wood
with wide green boughs
and a snowy hood.

I'll pin on a star
with five gold spurs
to mark my spruce
from the pines and firs.

I'll make me a score
of suet balls
to tie to my spruce
when the cold dusk falls,

And I'll hear next day
from the sheltering trees,
the Christmas carols
of the chickadees.

     —Aileen Fisher

THE SQUIRRELS' CHRISTMAS

The Squirrels had a Christmas tree,
   And Oh! it was so nice.
They spread it all with marzipan,
   And sprinkled it with spice.

They hung it o'er with fairy lamps
   And holly-berries red,
Apples and nuts and little cakes
   Tied on with golden thread.

They skipped and frisked and whisked about.
   It was a merry spree;
They ate up everything there was,
   Even the Christmas tree.

Only the fairy lamps were left
   To shine there in the snow.
I saw it all on Christmas Eve,
   And so, you see, I know!

            —Winifred Howard

GOLDEN COBWEBS

(AN OLD TALE RETOLD IN VERSE)

The Christmas tree stood by the parlor door,
    But the parlor door was locked
And the children could not get inside
    Even though they knocked.
For a Christmas tree must wait, folks say,
And not be seen till Christmas Day.
But the cat had seen the Christmas tree
    As she prowled the house by night,
And the dog had seen the Christmas tree
    By the moon's enchanting light;
And a little mouse beside her hole
Had looked at it with eyes of coal.
Even the spiders hoped to see
The secret, silent Christmas tree.
They planned, one day, to creep and crawl
Out of their cracks and up the wall
To get the highest view of all.
But just that day with mop and broom
The housemaid swept them from the room
And so the spiders could not see
The secret, silent Christmas tree.

The fairies heard the spiders weep,
    All on a winter's night,
Although their cries made softer sounds
    Than moth wings make in flight.
The fairies said: "Each living thing
That creeps, or crawls, or flaps a wing
Shall share the birthday of the King."

They took the spiders to the tree
   And, since they were too small
To see as far as cat or mouse,
   The fairies let them crawl
Along each twig and bending branch
   To look at every ball
And silver star and popcorn string;
And when they had seen everything
They thanked the fairies and went back
Each one to sleep inside his crack.

But, oh, the tree when they were gone
Was very sad to look upon!
Its branches were more gray than green
And little webs hung in between
That dulled the lights and all the sheen.

The fairies shook their heads and sighed,
For in their wisdom, ever wide,
They knew no housewife cared to see
Dull cobwebs on a Christmas tree.
They knew the children, too, would weep
To waken from their yuletide sleep
And glimpse a tree all bearded gray
That would not shine on Christmas Day. . . .

And so they turned the webs to gold
By waving fairy wands, I'm told;
And that is why there'll always be
Bright cobwebs on a Christmas tree.

—Rowena Bennett

JUNIPER

Who does not love the juniper tree?
The scent of its branches comes back to me,
And ever I think of the Holy Three
Who came to rest by the juniper tree!
Joseph and Mary and little wee Son
Came to rest when the day was done!
And the little Child slept on his Mother's knee
In the shelter sweet of the juniper tree!

—*Eileen Duggan*

THE LATCH-STRING'S
HANGING AT THE DOOR

Friends, we bid you come once more
   Oh, do! Oh, do!
The latch-string's hanging at the door
   For you! For you!
          —*Elsie Williams Chandler*

CHRISTMAS SINGING

We hang the holly up once more
   Oh, why? Oh, why?
To keep all evil from the door
   That's why! That's why!

We hang the mistletoe above
   Oh, why? Oh, why?
That all of us may dwell in love
   That's why! That's why!

We give the poor good things to eat
   Oh, why? Oh, why?
To warm their hearts and sauce our meat
   That's why! That's why!

We ring the bells on Christmas Day
   Oh, why? Oh, why?
To echo what the angels say
   On high! On high!

We light the candles on the tree
   Oh, why? Oh, why?
To light the Star for all to see
   That's why! That's why!

Friends, we bid you come once more
   Oh, do! Oh, do!
The latch-string's hanging at the door
   For you! For you!

—Elsie Williams Chandler

A CATCH BY THE HEARTH

Sing we all merrily
   Christmas is here,
The day that we love best
   Of days in the year.

Bring forth the holly,
   The box, and the bay,
Deck out our cottage
   For glad Christmas-day.

Sing we all merrily,
   Draw around the fire,
Sister and brother,
   Grandsire, and sire.
                    —*Author Unknown*

OLD CHRISTMASTIDE

Heap on more wood!—the wind is chill;
But let it whistle as it will
We'll keep our Christmas merry still.
                    —*Walter Scott*

DUCKLE, DUCKLE, DAISY [9]

Duckle, duckle, daisy
Martha must be crazy,
She went and made a Christmas cake
Of olive oil and gluten-flake,
And put it in the sink to bake,
Duckle, duckle, daisy.
                    —*Leroy F. Jackson*

I WASH MY FACE IN A GOLDEN VASE

I wash my face in a golden vase,
    All on a Christmas morning;
I wipe my face on a lily-white towel,
    All on a Christmas day.

I comb my hair with an ivory comb,
    All on a Christmas morning;
While two little ships were a-standing by,
    All on a Christmas day.

Oh, guess who was in one of them,
    All on a Christmas morning!
The Blessed Virgin and her Son,
    All on a Christmas day.

Then God looked down and said 'twas well,
    All on a Christmas morning;
'Now all my folks is saved from Hell.'
    All on a Christmas day.

—Author Unknown

OUR JOYFUL FEAST

So, now is come our joyful feast,
   Let every soul be jolly!
Each room with ivy leaves is drest,
   And every post with holly.

      *   *   *

Now all our neighbors' chimneys smoke,
   And Christmas logs are burning;
Their ovens with baked meats do choke,
   And all their spits are turning.
Without the door let sorrow lie,
And if for cold it hap to die,
We'll bury it in Christmas pie,
   And evermore be merry!

           —George Wither

AS I SAT UNDER A SYCAMORE TREE

As I sat under a sycamore tree, a sycamore tree, a sycamore tree,
I, looked me out upon the sea,
  A Christmas day in the morning.

I saw three ships a-sailing there, a-sailing there, a-sailing there,
The Virgin Mary and Christ they bare,
  A Christmas day in the morning.

He did whistle and she did sing, she did sing, she did sing,
And all the bells on earth did ring,
  A Christmas day in the morning.

And now we hope to taste your cheer, taste your cheer, taste your
      cheer,
And wish you all a happy New Year,
  A Christmas day in the morning.

                              —*Author Unknown*

CHRISTMAS

          My goodness, my goodness,
          It's Christmas again.
          The bells are all ringing.
          I do not know when
          I've been so excited.
          The tree is all fixed,
          The candles are lighted,
          The pudding is mixed.

The wreath's on the door
And the carols are sung,
The presents are wrapped
And the holly is hung.
The turkey is sitting
All safe in its pan,
And I am behaving
As calm as I can.
                    —*Marchette Chute*

DAY BEFORE CHRISTMAS

We have been helping with the cake
   And licking out the pan,
And wrapping up our packages
   As neatly as we can.
And we have hung our stockings up
   Beside the open grate,
And now there's nothing more to do
   Except
            To
                  Wait!
                  —*Marchette Chute*

JEST 'FORE CHRISTMAS

Father calls me William, sister calls me Will,
Mother calls me Willie, but the fellers call me Bill!
Mighty glad I ain't a girl—ruther be a boy,
Without them sashes, curls, an' things that's worn by
    Fauntleroy!
Love to chawnk green apples an' go swimmin' in the lake—
Hate to take the castor-ile they give for belly-ache!
'Most all the time, the whole year round, there ain't no
    flies on me,
But jest 'fore Christmas I'm as good as I kin be!

Got a yeller dog named Sport, sic him on the cat;
First thing she knows she doesn't know where she is at!
Got a clipper sled, an' when us kids goes out to slide,
'Long comes the grocery cart, an' we all hook a ride!
But sometimes when the grocery man is worrited an' cross,
He reaches at us with his whip, an' larrups up his hoss,
An' then I laff an' holler, "Oh, ye never teched *me!*"
But jest 'fore Christmas I'm as good as I kin be!

Gran'ma says she hopes that when I git to be a man,
I'll be a missionarer like her oldest brother, Dan,
As was et up by the cannibuls that lives in Ceylon's Isle,
Where every prospeck pleases, an' only man is vile!
But gran'ma she has never been to see a Wild West show,
Nor read the Life of Daniel Boone, or else I guess she'd
    know
That Buff'lo Bill an' cow-boys is good enough for me!
Excep' jest 'fore Christmas, when I'm good as I kin be!

And then old Sport he hangs around, so solemn-like an'
    still,
His eyes they seem a-sayin': "What's the matter, little Bill?"
The old cat sneaks down off her perch an' wonders what's
    become
Of them two enemies of hern that used to make things hum!
But I am so perlite an' 'tend so earnestly to biz,
That mother says to father: "How improved our Willie is!"
But father, havin' been a boy hisself, suspicions me
When, jest 'fore Christmas, I'm as good as I kin be!

For Christmas, with its lots an' lots of candies, cakes,
    an' toys,
Was made, they say, for proper kids, an' not for naughty
    boys;
So wash yer face an' bresh yer hair, an' mind yer p's and q's,
An' don't bust out yer pantaloons, and don't wear out yer
    shoes;
Say "Yessum" to the ladies, an' "Yessur" to the men,
An' when they's company, don't pass yer plate for pie again;
But, thinkin' of the things yer'd like to see upon that tree,
Jest 'fore Christmas be as good as yer kin be!

—Eugene Field

FOR CHRISTMAS DAY

A carol round the ruddy hearth,
  A song outside the door—
Let Christmas Day make sure its lay
  Sounds sweetly to the poor.

A turkey in the baking-tin,
  A pudding in the pot—
Let Christmas Day the hunger stay
  In them that have not got.

Red berries on the picture-frame,
  White berries in the hall—
Let Christmas Day look twice as gay
  With evergreens for all.

A stocking on the chimneypiece,
  A present on the chair—
Let Christmas Day not pass away
  Till those who have do share.

A star upon the midnight sky,
  A shepherd looking East—
On Christmas Day let all men pray,
  And not till after feast.

—*Eleanor Farjeon*

FOR THEM

Before you bid, for Christmas' sake,
Your guests to sit at meat,
Oh please to save a little cake
For them that have no treat.

Before you go down party-dressed
In silver gown or gold,
Oh please to send a little vest
To them that still go cold.

Before you give your girl and boy
Gay gifts to be undone,
Oh please to spare a little toy
To them that will have none.

Before you gather round the tree
To dance the day about,
Oh please to give a little glee
To them that go without.

—Eleanor Farjeon

HOLD, MEN, HOLD!

Hold, men, hold!
Be there loaf in your locker
And sheep in your fold,
A fire on your hearth,
And good luck for your lot,
Money in your pocket,
And a pudding in the pot!
Hold, men, hold!

Hold, men, hold! we are very cold,
Inside and outside it is very cold.
If you don't give us silver, then give us gold
From the money in your pockets.
Hold, men, hold!

God Almighty bless your hearth and fold,
Shut out the wolf, and keep out the cold!
Give us the silver and you keep the gold,
For 'tis money in your pockets!
Hold, men, hold!

—*Author Unknown*

CHRISTMAS CHANT

Candle, candle
  Burning bright
On our window
  Sill tonight,
Like the shining
  Christmas star
Guiding shepherds
  From afar,
Lead some weary
  Traveler here,
That he may share
  Our Christmas cheer.

         —*Isabel Shaw*

CHRISTMAS CAROL

God bless the master of this house,
  The mistress also,
And all the little children,
  That round the table go,
And all your kin and kinsmen
  That dwell both far and near;
I wish you a Merry Christmas
  And a Happy New Year.

         —*Author Unknown*

THIS HOLY NIGHT

God bless your house this holy night,
  And all within it;

God bless the candle that you light
  To midnight's minute:

The board at which you break your bread,
  The cup you drink of:

And as you raise it, the unsaid
  Name that you think of:

The warming fire, the bed of rest,
  The ringing laughter:

These things, and all things else be blest
  From floor to rafter

This holy night, from dark to light,
  Even more than other:

And, if you have no house to-night,
  God bless you, brother.
                              —*Eleanor Farjeon*

SANTA CLAUS COMES

I'm counting each day on my fingers
   and thumbs—
The weeks that must pass before Santa
   Claus comes.

*   —Author Unknown*

WHEN SANTA CLAUS COMES

A good time is coming, I wish it were here,
The very best time in the whole of the year;
I'm counting each day on my fingers and thumbs—
The weeks that must pass before Santa Claus comes.

Then when the first snowflakes begin to come down,
And the wind whistles sharp and the branches are brown,
I'll not mind the cold, though my fingers it numbs,
For it brings the time nearer when Santa Claus comes.
                    —*Author Unknown*

COME, RIDE WITH ME TO TOYLAND

Come, ride with me to Toyland,
    For this is Christmas Eve,
And just beyond the Dream Road
    (Where all is make-believe)
There lies a truly Toyland,
A real and wondrous Joyland,
A Little-Girl-and-Boy Land,
    Too lovely to conceive!

There Christmas fairies plant a tree
    That blossoms forth in stars
And comes to fruit in sugarplums;
There dolls and balls and painted drums
    And little trains of cars
All stand and wait for you and me
Beneath the shining wonder-tree.

So saddle up your hobby horse
    And ride across the night.
The thundering of our coursers' hoofs
    Will put the moon to flight;
And when the east is kitten-gray
    We'll sight that wondrous Joyland,
And at the break of Christmas Day
    We'll gallop into Toyland!

                —*Rowena Bennett*

STOCKING SONG ON CHRISTMAS EVE

Welcome, Christmas! heel and toe,
Here we wait thee in a row.
Come, good Santa Claus, we beg,—
Fill us tightly, foot and leg.

Fill us quickly ere you go,—
Fill us till we overflow.
That's the way! and leave us more
Heaped in piles upon the floor.

Little feet that ran all day
Twitch in dreams of merry play;
Little feet that jumped at will
Lie all pink, and warm, and still.

See us, how we lightly swing;
Hear us, how we try to sing.
Welcome, Christmas! heel and toe,
Come and fill us ere you go.

Here we hang till some one nimbly
Jumps with treasure down the chimney.
Bless us! how he'll tickle us!
Funny old St. Nicholas!

—*Mary Mapes Dodge*

A CHRISTMAS WISH

I'd like a stocking made for a giant,
And a meeting house full of toys,
Then I'd go out in a happy hunt
For the poor little girls and boys;
Up the street and down the street,
And across and over the town,
I'd search and find them every one,
Before the sun went down.

One would want a new jack-knife
Sharp enough to cut;
One would long for a doll with hair,
And eyes that open and shut;
One would ask for a china set
With dishes all to her mind;
One would wish a Noah's ark
With beasts of every kind.

Some would like a doll's cook-stove
And a little toy wash tub;
Some would prefer a little drum,
For a noisy rub-a-dub;
Some would wish for a story book,
And some for a set of blocks;
Some would be wild with happiness
Over a new tool-box.

And some would rather have little shoes,
And other things warm to wear;
For many children are very poor
And the winter is hard to bear;
I'd buy soft flannels for little frocks,
And a thousand stockings or so,
And the jolliest little coats and cloaks
To keep out the frost and snow.

I'd load a wagon with caramels
And candy of every kind,
And buy all the almond and pecan nuts
And taffy that I could find;
And barrels and barrels of oranges
I'd scatter right in the way,
So the children would find them the
        very first thing
When they awake on Christmas day.
                    —*Eugene Field*

FOR CHRISTMAS

I want a Puppy Dog
Not made of wool.
I want a Kitty Cat
I don't have to wind.
I want a Nanny Goat
I don't have to pull;
And I want an Elephant
Can sit DOWN behind.
                    —*Dorothy Aldis*

SANTA CLAUS AND THE MOUSE

One Christmas eve, when Santa Claus
  Came to a certain house,
To fill the children's stockings there,
  He found a little mouse.

"A merry Christmas, little friend,"
  Said Santa, good and kind.
"The same to you, sir," said the mouse;
  "I thought you wouldn't mind

"If I should stay awake to-night
  And watch you for a while."
"You're very welcome, little mouse,"
  Said Santa, with a smile.

And then he filled the stockings up
  Before the mouse could wink—
From toe to top, from top to toe,
  There wasn't left a chink.

"Now, they won't hold another thing,"
  Said Santa Claus, with pride.
A twinkle came in mouse's eyes,
  But humbly he replied:

"It's not polite to contradict—
  Your pardon I implore—
But in the fullest stocking there
  J could put one thing more."

"Oh, ho!" laughed Santa, "silly mouse!
  Don't I know how to pack?
By filling stockings all these years,
  I should have learned the knack."

And then he took the stocking down
  From where it hung so high,
And said: "Now put in one thing more;
  I give you leave to try."

The mousie chuckled to himself,
  And then he softly stole
Right to the stocking's crowded toe
  And gnawed a little hole!

"Now, if you please, good Santa Claus,
  I've put in one thing more;
For you will own that little hole
  Was not in there before."

How Santa Claus did laugh and laugh!
  And then he gaily spoke:
"Well! you shall have a Christmas cheese
  For that nice little joke."

If you don't think this story true,
  Why! I can show to you
The *very stocking* with the hole
  The little mouse gnawed through.
  —*Emilie Poulsson*

KRIS KRINGLE

Kris Kringle comes with loads of toys
For all the little girls and boys,
And though we know not where he's from
We're glad to have Kris Kringle come.
  —*Clinton Scollard*

SANTA CLAUS

He comes in the night! He comes in the night!
   He softly, silently comes;
While the little brown heads on the pillows so white
   Are dreaming of bugles and drums.
He cuts through the snow like a ship through the foam,
   While the white flakes around him whirl;
Who tells him I know not, but he findeth the home
   Of each good little boy and girl.

His sleigh it is long, and deep, and wide;
   It will carry a host of things,
While dozens of drums hang over the side,
   With the sticks sticking under the strings.
And yet not the sound of a drum is heard,
   Not a bugle blast is blown,
As he mounts to the chimney-top like a bird,
   And drops to the hearth like a stone.

The little red stockings he silently fills,
   Till the stockings will hold no more;
The bright little sleds for the great snow hills
   Are quickly set down on the floor.
Then Santa Claus mounts to the roof like a bird,
   And glides to his seat in the sleigh;
Not a sound of a bugle or drum is heard
   As he noiselessly gallops away.

He rides to the East, and he rides to the West,
   Of his goodies he touches not one;
He eateth the crumbs of the Christmas feast
   When the dear little folks are done.
Old Santa Claus doeth all that he can;
   This beautiful mission is his;
Then, children be good to the little old man,
   When you find who the little man is.
                              —*Author Unknown*

OLD SANTA IS AN ACTIVE MAN

Old Santa is an active man,
   He slides down chimneys black,
Fills stockings while his reindeer wait,
   And then goes climbing back!
                              —*Lois Lenski*

A VISIT FROM ST. NICHOLAS

'Twas the night before Christmas, when all through the house
Not a creature was stirring, not even a mouse;
The stockings were hung by the chimney with care,
In hopes that St. Nicholas soon would be there;
The children were nestled all snug in their beds,
While visions of sugar-plums danced in their heads;
And mamma in her 'kerchief, and I in my cap,
Had just settled our brains for a long winter's nap,
When out on the lawn there arose such a clatter,
I sprang from the bed to see what was the matter.
Away to the window I flew like a flash,
Tore open the shutters and threw up the sash.
The moon on the breast of the new-fallen snow
Gave the lustre of mid-day to objects below,
When, what to my wondering eyes should appear,
But a miniature sleigh, and eight tiny reindeer,
With a little old driver, so lively and quick,
I knew in a moment it must be St. Nick.
More rapid than eagles his coursers they came,
And he whistled, and shouted, and called them by name;
"Now, *Dasher!* now, *Dancer!* now, *Prancer* and *Vixen!*
On, *Comet!* on, *Cupid!* on, *Donder* and *Blitzen!*
To the top of the porch! to the top of the wall!
Now dash away! dash away! clash away all!"
As dry leaves that before the wild hurricane fly,
When they meet with an obstacle, mount to the sky,
So up to the house-top the coursers they flew,
With the sleigh full of toys, and St. Nicholas too.
And then, in a twinkling, I heard on the roof
The prancing and pawing of each little hoof.
As I drew in my head, and was turning around,
Down the chimney St. Nicholas came with a bound.

He was dressed all in fur, from his head to his foot,
And his clothes were all tarnished with ashes and soot;
A bundle of toys he had flung on his back,
And he looked like a peddler just opening his pack.
His eyes—how they twinkled! his dimples how merry!
His cheeks were like roses, his nose like a cherry!
His droll little mouth was drawn up like a bow,
And the beard of his chin was as white as the snow;
The stump of a pipe he held tight in his teeth,
And the smoke it encircled his head like a wreath;
He had a broad face and a little round belly,
That shook, when he laughed, like a bowlful of jelly.
He was chubby and plump, a right jolly old elf,
And I laughed when I saw him, in spite of myself;
A wink of his eye and a twist of his head,
Soon gave me to know I had nothing to dread;
He spoke not a word, but went straight to his work,
And filled all the stockings; then turned with a jerk;
And laying his finger aside of his nose
And giving a nod, up the chimney he rose;
He sprang to his sleigh, to his team gave a whistle,
And away they all flew like the down of a thistle,
But I heard him exclaim, ere he drove out of sight,
"Happy Christmas to all, and to all a good-night."
—Clement Clarke Moore

A REAL SANTA CLAUS

Santa Claus, I hang for you,
By the mantel, stockings two:
One for me and one to go
To another boy I know.

There's a chimney in the town
You have never traveled down.
Should you chance to enter there
You would find a room all bare:
Not a stocking could you spy,
Matters not how you might try;
And the shoes, you'd find are such
As no boy would care for much.
In a broken bed you'd see
Some one just about like me,
Dreaming of the pretty toys
Which you bring to other boys,
And to him a Christmas seems
Merry only in his dreams.

All he dreams then, Santa Claus,
Stuff the stocking with, because
When it's filled up to the brim
I'll be Santa Claus to him!

—*Frank Dempster Sherman*

CHRISTMAS BROWNIE

There was a Christmas Brownie—
    (Heigh-ho for little people!)
His hair was bright and downy
    As snow upon a steeple.
His laugh was like a sleigh bell,
    As tinkly and as merry.
His cheeks were round and rosy
    As any holly berry.

There was a Christmas Brownie—
    (Heigh-ho for little elves!)
One year he helped old Santa
    Take down from off his shelves
The Christmas toys for girls and boys
    And pack them in the sleigh—
One year he drove with Santa Claus
    Till break of Christmas Day.

But when they reached the last, last house
    (A house of fisher folk),
Old Santa dropped the last, last doll,
    And with a crash it broke!
"What shall I do?" poor Santa cried.
    "This Mary girl's a dear.
I'd go back for another doll,
    But morning's almost here."

As Santa shed a sorry tear,
    The little Brownie spoke:
"Since it's so late, we can't do much
    About the doll we broke.
But I'm as tall as any doll,
    And light as any fairy.

So let me climb the Christmas tree
  And be a gift for Mary!"

And so he stayed with fisher folk
  And thought it was quite jolly
By night to be a Brownie boy,
  By day to be a dolly.
Then sing a song for Christmas time
  (Heigh-ho for fay and elf!)
But sing your best for Brownie boy,
  Because he gave himself.
                    —*Rowena Bennett*

CHRISTMAS MORNING

This is the magic morning—
  Tumble out of bed,
Tiptoe down the long stairs
  Softly on each tread.
Oh, what's this before you?
  Rub your sleepy eyes—
Golden lights and silver,
  Beautiful surprise!
Sparkling tree of wonder,
  Gifts, enchanting, new—
Magic, magic morning,
  Christmas Dream come true!
                    —*Elsie Melchert Fowler*

FRIENDLY BEASTS
AROUND HIM STOOD

Christmas morn, the legends say,

Even the cattle kneel to pray,

Even the wildest beast afar

Knows the light of the Saviour's star.

—*Denis A. McCarthy*

CHRISTMAS IN THE WOODS

Tonight when the hoar frost falls on the wood,
And the rabbit cowers, and the squirrel is cold,
And the horned owl huddles against a star,
And the drifts are deep, and the year is old,
All shy creatures will think of Him.
The shivering mouse, the hare, the wild young fox,
The doe with the startled fawn,
Will dream of gentleness and a Child:

The buck with budding horns will turn
His starry eyes to a silver hill tonight,
The chipmunk will awake and stir
And leave his burrow for the chill, dark midnight,
And all timid things will pause and sigh, and sighing, bless
That Child who loves the trembling hearts,
The shy hearts of the wilderness.

                              —*Frances Frost*

ONE NIGHT

Last winter when the snow was deep
    And sparkled on the lawn
And there was moonlight everywhere,
    I saw a little fawn.

I watched her playing in the snow.
    She did not want to leave.
She must have known before she came
    That it was Christmas Eve.

                              —*Marchette Chute*

THE LAMB-CHILD

When Christ the Babe was born,
　　Full many a little lamb,
Upon the wintry hills forlorn,
　　Was nestled near its dam;
And, waking or asleep,
　　Upon His mother's breast,
For love of her, each mother-sheep
　　And baby-lamb He blessed.
　　　　　　　　—John B. Tabb

TWELFTH NIGHT

(THE SONG OF THE CAMELS)

Not born to the forest are we,
Not born to the plain,
To the grass and the shadowed tree
And the splashing of rain.
Only the sand we know
And the cloudless sky,
The mirage and the deep-sunk well
And the stars on high.

To the sound of our bells we came
With huge soft stride,
Kings riding upon our backs,
Slaves at our side,
Out of the East drawn on
By a dream and a star,
Seeking the hills and the groves
Where the fixed towns are.

Our goal was no palace gate,
No temple of old,
But a child in his mother's lap,
In the cloudy cold.
The olives were windy and white,
Dust swirled through the town,
As all in their royal robes
Our masters knelt down.

Then back to the desert we paced
In our phantom state,
And faded again in the sands
That are secret as fate—
Portents of glory and danger
Our dark shadows lay
At the feet of the babe in the manger,
And then drifted away.

—Elizabeth Coatsworth

EERILY SWEET

The cocks are crowing
To the stars,
One crows to Venus,
And one to Mars,

Like trumpets blown
Across the snow
Eerily sweet
The proud cocks crow.

"It is not dawn
O birds of the sun!
On the Milky Way
Still flies the Swan,

"And great Orion
Strides through the air,
And Berenice
Lets down her hair.

"It is not dawn
O birds of the day!
Why do you crow
With the sun far away?"

The cocks crow loud
And the cocks crow clear
Across the snow
'Tis a joy to hear.

"Once long ago
When the world was young
Over a manger
A bright star hung.

"Marvelled both man
  And beast at the sight,
  But the cocks saluted
  The holy light.

"Proudly they stood
  And clapped their wings
  To welcome the star
  Of the King of Kings!

"And now sometimes
  Across the snow
  We remember that night
  And rise, and crow,

"And repeat the chant
  To that star thrice blest—
'Christus, Christus
  Natus est!' "

  Like trumpets blown
  Across the snow
  Eerily sweet
  The proud cocks crow.
                    —*Elizabeth Coatsworth*

CHRISTMAS SONG

Of all the animals on earth
I think the luckiest
Are the ox and ass who had
Young Jesus for their guest,
The ox and ass in Bethlehem
Whose privilege and joy
It was to share their stable with
A little homeless Boy;
The luckiest of animals
On earth, both tame and wild,
For they were first to look with love
Upon the Christmas Child!

—*Elizabeth-Ellen Long*

THE FRIENDLY BEASTS

Jesus our brother, strong and good,
Was humbly born in a stable rude,
And the friendly beasts around Him stood,
Jesus our brother, strong and good.

"I," said the donkey, shaggy and brown,
"I carried His mother up hill and down,
I carried her safely to Bethlehem town;
I," said the donkey, shaggy and brown.

"I," said the cow, all white and red,
"I gave Him my manger for His bed,
I gave Him my hay to pillow His head,
"I," said the cow, all white and red.

"I," said the sheep, with curly horn,
"I gave Him my wool for His blanket warm,
He wore my coat on Christmas morn;
"I," said the sheep, with curly horn.

"I," said the dove, from the rafters high,
"Cooed Him to sleep, my mate and I,
We cooed Him to sleep, my mate and I;
I," said the dove, from the rafters high.

And every beast, by some good spell,
In the stable dark was glad to tell,
Of the gift he gave Immanuel,
The gift he gave Immanuel.

—Author Unknown

IN THE STABLE

There was a pussy in the stable
When Christ was born.
There was an ox there and a donkey,
In the grey dawn.
But there was a pussy there also,
That Christmas morn.

And there was a mouse in the corner,
Still with surprise.
And by the door there was a brown dog,
Old and so wise.
He peeped through the fur on his forehead
With such bright eyes.

And there was a little bird there too,
With a red breast,
And with its beak it pulled out feathers
To make a nest,
To help Mary make for her Baby
A place to rest.

All the animals gave all they could
On Christmas day.
The ox and the ass gave their stable
And their sweet hay.
The pussy cat purred a lullaby
Loving and gay.

And the loyal old dog kept unsleeping
Watch by the door,
And the mouse kept so still in wonder
There on the floor.
Their service cried out to the Baby,
I love and adore.

74

They knew that He could not say thank you,
He was too weak,
Yet they knew He thanked them and loved them,
Humble and meek.
They knew He was God the Almighty
Come love to seek.

—*Elizabeth Goudge*

THE BARN

"I am tired of this barn!" said the colt.
"And every day it snows.
  Outside there's no grass any more
  And icicles grow on my nose.
  I am tired of hearing the cows
  Breathing and talking together.
  I am sick of these clucking hens.
  I *hate* stables and winter weather!"

"Hush, little colt," said the mare
"And a story I will tell
  Of a barn like this one of ours
  And the wonders that there befell.
  It was weather much like this
  And the beasts stood as we stand now
  In the warm good dark of the barn—
  A horse and an ass and a cow."

"And sheep?" asked the colt. "Yes, sheep
  And a pig and a goat and a hen.
  All of the beasts of the barnyard,
  The usual servants of men.
  And into their midst came a lady
  And she was as cold as death

75

But the animals leaned above her
And made her warm with their breath.

"There was her baby born
And laid to sleep in the hay
While music flooded the rafters
And the barn was as light as day.
And angels and kings and shepherds
Came to worship the babe from afar,
But we looked at him first of all creatures
By the bright strange light of a star!"

—*Elizabeth Coatsworth*

CHRISTMAS LEGENDS

Christmas morn, the legends say,
Even the cattle kneel to pray,
Even the beasts of wood and field
Homage to Christ the Saviour yield.
Horse and cow and woolly sheep
Wake themselves from their heavy sleep,
Bending heads and knees to Him
Who came to earth in a stable dim.
Far away in the forest dark
Creatures timidly wake and hark,
Feathered bird and furry beast
Turn their eyes to the mystic East.
Loud at the dawning, chanticleer
Sounds his note, the rest of the year,
But Christmas Eve the whole night long
Honouring Christ he sings his song.
Christmas morn, the legends say,
Even the cattle kneel to pray,
Even the wildest beast afar
Knows the light of the Saviour's star.

—*Denis A. McCarthy*

LEGENDS OF CHRISTMAS

On Christmas Eve while hamlets sleep
The wild bees wake and sing,
Above the frosty fields they sweep,
To praise a newborn King . . .
But none except the pure of heart,
With insight where to go,
But none except the pure of heart
    may know.

On Christmas, at the quiet hours,
The valley and the hill
Turn blue with hosts of starry flowers
That out of heaven spill . . .
But none except the pure of heart,
With eyes of clarity,
But none except the pure of heart
    may see.

On Christmas Eve at twelve o'clock
The cattle kneel to pray,
And lamb and ox and crowing cock
Have human words to say . . .
But none except the pure of heart,
Who have an inner ear,
But none except the pure of heart
    may hear.

              —*Aileen Fisher*

WHO WILL KNEEL THEM
GENTLY DOWN

Shall I tell you who will come
    to Bethlehem on Christmas Morn,
who will kneel them gently down
    before the Lord, new-born?
         —*Ruth Sawyer*, TRANS.

BETHLEHEM OF JUDEA

A little child,
  A shining star.
A stable rude,
  The door ajar.

Yet in that place,
  So crude, forlorn,
The Hope of all
  The world was born.
            —*Author Unknown*

ABOVE THE STABLE

Above the stable,
  Angels sing,
Inside the manger
  Lies a King!

Lies an Infant,
  Meek and lowly
Lies a Sovereign
  High and Holy!
            —*Nona Keen Duffy*

MARY'S LULLABY

Little Dove,
   Little Darling,
Little Sparrow,
   Little Starling,
Little Light,
   Little Joy,
Little Treasure,
   Little Boy.
                —*Ivy O. Eastwick*

THE SMALLEST ANGEL

The smallest angel saw them go—
Stepping, dignified and slow
Down the shining golden stair,
Through the frosty midnight air.

"Fear not! fear not! To you we bring
Tidings of a new-born King."
Cherubim and seraphim
Chanted thus their Christmas hymn.

The smallest angel saw them go—
Stepping, dignified and slow
Then, down the shining banister
He slid with tiny wings a-whir

Down to where the Baby lay
Snug and warm in fragrant hay.
"Fear not!" he whispered, "little King,
You are the tidings that they bring!"
                —*Elsie Binns*

THE BIRTHDAY OF THE LORD

The Baby Christ, when He was born,
　　Was cradled in a manger—
Still He was King of all the world—
　　Was ever story stranger?

The shepherds came from far and wide,
　　And, wondering, bent above Him;
His will it was that hearts of men
　　Should know Him and should love Him.

The cattle breathed their breath on Him;
　　The little lambs pressed near Him;
His will it was that man nor beast
　　Should stand apart nor fear Him;

Then let your hearts be filled with joy,
　　While Christmas bells are ringing,
And keep the birthday of the Lord
　　With merriment and singing.

—Mary Jane Carr

"LOS PASTORES"

Let me tell to you the story
How one night I saw the shepherds
Going walking, walking, walking
    To the manger in Belén.

Came one angel very splendid,
With his white wings spread and shining,
Saying, "Hurry, shepherds, hurry,
    To the manger in Belén."

But then came the old *diablo*,
Splendid also in his red coat,
Saying, "Shepherds, do not hurry
    To the manger in Belén."

San Miguel, he fought the devil
With a long sword, swift and deadly;
So the shepherds went on walking
    To the manger in Belén.

One old shepherd was so sleepy
He lay down beside the roadway,
And they almost had to push him
    To the manger in Belén.

At the end of all the waiting,
At the end of all the walking,
Last they found the Mother Mary
    With that carpenter, José.

Then they looked and looked in wonder
At the little holy baby;
And they all went kneeling, kneeling
    At the manger in Belén.

              —*Edith Agnew*

84

THE RIDING OF THE KINGS

In a far land upon a day,
Where never snow did fall,
Three Kings went riding on the way
Bearing presents all.

And one wore red, and one wore gold,
And one was clad in green,
And one was young, and one was old,
And one was in between.

The middle one had human sense,
The young had loving eyes,
The old had much experience,
And all of them were wise.

Choosing no guide by eve and morn
But heaven's starry drifts,
They rode to find the Newly-Born
For whom they carried gifts.

Oh, far away in time they rode
Upon their wanderings,
And still in story goes abroad
The riding of the Kings.

So wise, that in their chosen hour,
As through the world they filed,
They sought not wealth or place or power,
But rode to find a Child.

—*Eleanor Farjeon*

THE SHEPHERD LEFT BEHIND

"The hour is late," the shepherds said,
  "And the miles are long to wind;
Do you stay here with the sheep, instead!"
  And they left the lad behind.

He heard their feet in the dark ravine,
  The drop of the sheepfold bars,
And then blue stillness flowed between
  The huddled sheep and stars.

He sat him down to wait for dawn,
  His crook across his knees,
And thought of the shepherds moving on
  Under the olive trees.

Herding his flocks in Palestine,
  He thought, that lad of old,
How some must follow the Angel's sign
  And some must tend the fold.

And as he mused he took his pipe—
  'Twas a shepherd's pipe he had—
And there, while the frosty stars grew ripe
  And shone on the shepherd lad,

The first sweet Christmas carol twined
  From the willow's slender stem—
Blown by the shepherd left behind—
  To a Babe in Bethlehem.

—Mildred Plew Merryman

A CHRISTMAS FOLK-SONG

The little Jesus came to town;
The wind blew up, the wind blew down;
Out in the street the wind was bold;
Now who would house Him from the cold?

Then opened wide a stable door,
Fair were the rushes on the floor;
The Ox put forth a hornèd head;
"Come, Little Lord, here make Thy bed."

Up rose the Sheep were folded near:
"Thou Lamb of God, come, enter here."
He entered there to rush and read,
Who was the Lamb of God indeed.

The little Jesus came to town;
With Ox and Sheep He laid Him down;
Peace to the byre, peace to the fold,
For that they housed Him from the cold!

—Lizette Woodworth Reese

LONG, LONG AGO

Winds thro' the olive trees
   Softly did blow,
Round little Bethlehem
   Long, long ago.

Sheep on the hillside lay
   Whiter than snow;
Shepherds were watching them,
   Long, long ago.

Then from the happy sky,
   Angels bent low,
Singing their songs of joy,
   Long, long ago.

For in a manger bed,
   Cradled we know,
Christ came to Bethlehem,
   Long, long ago.

            —*Author Unknown*

CHRISTMAS MORNING

If Bethlehem were here today,
Or this were very long ago,
There wouldn't be a winter time
Nor any cold or snow.

I'd run out through the garden gate,
And down along the pasture walk;
And off beside the cattle barns
I'd hear a kind of gentle talk.

I'd move the heavy iron chain
And pull away the wooden pin;
I'd push the door a little bit
And tiptoe very softly in.

The pigeons and the yellow hens
And all the cows would stand away;
Their eyes would open wide to see
A lady in the manger hay,

If this were very long ago
And Bethlehem were here today.

And Mother held my hand and smiled—
I mean the lady would—and she
Would take the woolly blankets off
Her little boy so I could see.

His shut-up eyes would be asleep,
And he would look like our John,
And he would be all crumpled too,
And have a pinkish color on.

I'd watch his breath go in and out.
His little clothes would all be white.
I'd slip my finger in his hand
To feel how he could hold it tight.

And she would smile and say, "Take care,"
The mother, Mary, would, "Take care";
And I would kiss his little hand
And touch his hair.

While Mary put the blankets back
The gentle talk would soon begin.
And when I'd tiptoe softly out
I'd meet the wise men going in.

—Elizabeth Madox Roberts

A CHRISTMAS CAROL

The Christ-child lay on Mary's lap,
  His hair was like a light.
(O weary, weary were the world,
  But here is all aright.)

The Christ-child lay on Mary's breast,
  His hair was like a star.
(O stern and cunning are the kings,
  But here the true hearts are.)

The Christ-child lay on Mary's heart,
  His hair was like a fire.
(O weary, weary is the world,
  But here the world's desire.)

The Christ-child stood at Mary's knee,
  His hair was like a crown,
And all the flowers looked up at Him
  And all the stars looked down.

              —Gilbert K. Chesterton

CRADLE HYMN

Away in a manger,
No crib for a bed,
The little Lord Jesus
Lay down his sweet head;
The stars in the heavens
Looked down where he lay,
The little Lord Jesus
Asleep in the hay.

The cattle are lowing,
The poor baby wakes,
But little Lord Jesus
No crying he makes.
I love thee, Lord Jesus,
Look down from the sky,
And stay by my cradle
Till morning is nigh.

—*Martin Luther*

It's not what you give but how you give

MY GIFT

What can I give Him
Poor as I am;
If I were a shepherd,
I would give Him a lamb.
If I were a wise man,
I would do my part.
But what can I give Him?
I will give Him my heart.

—*Christina G. Rossetti*

92

CHRISTMAS EVE

And there were in the same country shepherds
    abiding in the field, keeping watch over
    their flock by night.
And, lo, the angel of the Lord came upon them,
    and the glory of the Lord shone round
    about them: and they were sore afraid.
And the angel said unto them, Fear not: for, be-
    hold, I bring you good tidings of great
    joy, which shall be to all people.
For unto you is born this day in the city of David
    a Saviour, which is Christ the Lord.
And this *shall be* a sign unto you; Ye shall find the
    babe wrapped in swaddling clothes, lying
    in a manger.
And suddenly there was with the angel a multi-
    tude of the heavenly host praising God,
    and saying,
Glory to God in the highest, and on earth peace,
    good will toward men.
                   —*The Bible*   Luke 2: 8-14

CHRISTMAS LEGEND

The Baby King Jesus came down to His own,
A stable His palace, a manger His throne,
The city about Him was slumbering deep,
But every dear baby laughed out in its sleep.
And so on each Christmas, from then ever after,
The world wakens up to the children's sweet laughter.
                              —*Edna Randolph Worrell*

WORDS FROM AN OLD SPANISH CAROL

Shall I tell you who will come
    to Bethlehem on Christmas Morn,
who will kneel them gently down
    before the Lord, new-born?

One small fish from the river,
    with scales of red, red gold,
one wild bee from the heather,
    one grey lamb from the fold,
one ox from the high pasture,
    one black bull from the herd,
one goatling from the far hills,
    one white, white bird.

And many children—God give them grace,
bringing tall candles to light Mary's face.

Shall I tell you who will come
    to Bethlehem on Christmas Morn,
who will kneel them gently down
    before the Lord, new-born?
                              —*Ruth Sawyer, trans.*

NOT ONLY
IN THE CHRISTMAS-TIDE

Each season held its light divine,
  Its glow of love and cheer;
For Christ, who lived for all the world,
  Was part of all the year.
                    —*Mary Mapes Dodge*

NOT ONLY IN THE CHRISTMAS-TIDE

Not only in the Christmas-tide
    The holy baby lay;
But month by month his home he blessed,
    And brightened every day.
Each season held its light divine,
    Its glow of love and cheer;
For Christ, who lived for all the world,
    Was part of all the year.

                —Mary Mapes Dodge

CONVERSATION BETWEEN
MR. AND MRS. SANTA CLAUS
(OVERHEARD AT THE NORTH POLE EARLY CHRISTMAS MORNING)

"Are the reindeer in the rain, dear?"
Asked Mrs. Santa Claus.
"No. I put them in the barn, dear,
To dry their little paws."

"Is the sleigh, sir, put away, sir,
In the barn beside the deer?"
"Yes, I'm going to get it ready
To use again next year."

"And the pack, dear, is it back, dear?"
"Yes. It's empty of its toys,
And tomorrow I'll start filling it,
For next year's girls and boys."

—*Rowena Bennett*

AFTER-CHRISTMAS POEM

Put away the Christ Child,
  Lay His Mother by.
Wrap in tissue paper
  The Star which shone on high.

Take down the wooden stable,
  The manger, too, but leave
Something of His love to last
  Until next Christmas Eve!
                    —*Elizabeth-Ellen Long*

DISCARDED CHRISTMAS TREE

(A SONG FOR ANY ALLEY AFTER THE HOLIDAYS)

Fall gently, rain, on leaf and limb
Which gave up growing just for Him.
Blow softly, wind, upon the tree
Which died for His nativity.

For though cast off by us, at will,
With no one caring, yet it still,
Of all green things remains the one
Which wore a Star for God's own Son!
                    —*Elizabeth-Ellen Long*

ASHES OF THE CHRISTMAS TREE

When Christmas trees at last are burned
Upon the hearth, they leap and flash
More brilliantly than other wood,
And wear a difference in the ash.

They do not lie in pallid gray,
But rise above the flames—oh, see!
They lift like clouds of silver moths,
For they have been the Christmas tree.
                    —*Yetza Gillespie*

THE CHRISTMAS EXCHANGE

When Bill gives me a book, I know
It's just the book he wanted, so
When I give him a ping-pong set,
He's sure it's what I hoped to get.

Then after Christmas we arrange
A little Christmas Gift Exchange;
I give the book to him, and he
Gives back the ping-pong set to me.

So each gives twice—and that is pleasant—
To get the truly-wanted present.
                    —*Arthur Guiterman*

PRESENTS

I wanted a rifle for Christmas,
  I wanted a bat and a ball,
I wanted some skates and a bicycle,
  But I didn't want mittens at all.

    I wanted a whistle
      And I wanted a kite,
    I wanted a pocketknife
      That shut up tight.
    I wanted some boots
      And I wanted a kit,
But I didn't want mittens one little bit.

I told them I didn't like mittens,
  I told them as plain as plain.
I told them I didn't WANT mittens,
  And they've given me mittens again!
          —*Marchette Chute*

SCHOOL AFTER CHRISTMAS

Christmas comes
　　And goes away too soon.
I wish that it
　　Would come again in June.

I'm very fond
　　Of *every* Holiday
But Christmas time
　　Is different in a way.

There's Santa Claus
　　And all the toys he brings;
The Christmas tree
　　And—oh, a thousand things!

But every time
　　It's over with so soon.

I wish—I wish
　　It came again in June.
                    —Wymond Garthwaite

THE JOY OF GIVING

Somehow, not only for Christmas
   But all the long year through,
The joy that you give to others
   Is the joy that comes back to you;
And the more you spend in blessing
   The poor and lonely and sad,
The more of your heart's possessing
   Returns to make you glad.

—John Greenleaf Whittier

INDEX OF AUTHORS

INDEX OF TITLES

110

INDEX OF FIRST LINES

113

114